Dear Cindy

Thought this might be
kind of fun - remember
no cheating !

Merry Christmas
        Love
        Kim

S0-AVJ-698

3⁹⁶
5-8

YOU BE THE
JUDGE

The Curtis Publishing Company,
Indianapolis, Indiana

YOU BE THE JUDGE

Legal Brainteasers from
THE SATURDAY EVENING POST

You be the Judge
Editor: Judy Newton
Art Director: Jinny Sauer Hoffman
Editorial Staff: Louise Fortson, Jean White and Jacquelyn Sibert
Art and Production: Kay Douglas and Greg Vanzo
Compositors: Gloria McCoy, Geri Watson, Penny Allison and
Kathy Simpson

Copyright ©1979 by The Curtis Publishing Company. All rights reserved.
No part of this book may be used or reproduced in any manner whatsoever
without written permission except in the case of brief quotations embodied
in critical articles and reviews. Printed in The United States of America.
For information address The Curtis Publishing Company, Inc.,
1100 Waterway Boulevard, Indianapolis, Indiana 46202.
Library of Congress Catalog Card Number 79-53768 ISBN 0-89387-035-8.

Table of Contents

The Neighborly Way?

Louder than a Lawn Mower

After a bitter quarrel with her next-door neighbors, the McFloys, Mrs. Flamm began an all-out war to force them to move. She trained her dog to howl outside their bedroom window nights. She herself arose at daybreak and ran her noisy lawn mower up and down to make sure that the McFloys got no sleep at all.

Tried beyond endurance, the McFloys sued both Mr. and

Mrs. Flamm for damages, although Flamm himself had taken no part in the feud.

"Why drag Flamm into it?" the attorney for the Flamms demanded at the trial. "Granted that Mrs. Flamm has no defense for her malicious actions, there is no reason for holding her husband liable. He remained strictly neutral, and the case against him should be dismissed."

"Is Flamm a man or a mouse?" opposing counsel countered. "Instead of staying neutral, he should have put a stop to his wife's outrageous conduct. As he, not she, has the money, we want a judgment against both of them so as to be sure to collect."

If you were the judge, would you make Flamm share the responsibility for his wife's behavior?

William Donaldson

Watch Out, Caruso!

The Pottses rented one of two unused bedrooms in the Kettleses' home with the understanding that they would share the only bathroom. Nothing was said about renting the other bedroom to another party. One morning Mrs. Potts heard an unfamiliar off-key baritone voice in the bathroom. Peeking through the door, she spied a strange man singing happily in the bathtub.

"Our new lodger," Mrs. Kettles explained, when asked who was doing the singing.

"Outrageous!" Mrs. Potts snapped. "When we moved in, nothing was said about sharing the bathroom with a stranger."

"Either he shares the bathroom or you move out!" Mrs. Kettles snapped back.

When the Pottses refused to do either, the Kettleses instituted court action to evict them.

"There was no agreement giving the Pottses the exclusive privilege of sharing the bathroom with us alone," the Kettleses contended. "So we had every right to extend the same privilege to our new lodger. The Pottses' refusal to share with him interferes with our right to run our property in our own way, so they should get out."

"Sharing a bathroom is such a personal matter," the Pottses replied, "that we felt justified in assuming that the privilege was not extended to anyone else. Hence we don't feel that we should be forced to move."

If you were the judge, would you let the Pottses stay?

William Donaldson

Friendly Persuasion

When Francis came home from the movies, five narcotics agents with drawn pistols arrested him. Asked if he would permit them to search his home, he nervously agreed, although he knew he had a constitutional right to refuse. The agents found incriminating evidence and presented it at the trial. Counsel for Francis objected.

"This evidence is the result of an illegal search and seizure made against Francis' will," defense counsel asserted. "He was overawed at the time."

"On the contrary, it was obtained with Francis' expressed consent and permission," the prosecutor countered. "He knew exactly what he was doing."

If you were the judge, would you rule out the evidence?

José Schorr

Water, Water Everywhere

"Henry," Mrs. Podsnap wailed, "we'll never have a garden at this rate. Every time it rains the water runs downhill from the Overtops' yard and washes our plants right out of the ground."

"Now don't you worry, honey," Henry soothed. "All we have to do is to put up an embankment at the back of our garden to keep the water from running down from their yard into ours."

Henry's embankment, when completed, not only held back the unwelcome water but caused it to back up until the Overtops' yard looked like a lake instead of a lawn.

"Tear down that dike!" Overtop roared. "You're flooding my place!"

When Henry refused to comply, Overtop sought a court order to compel him to remove the embankment. He argued:

"The rain that doesn't soak into the ground is bound to run downhill. Henry knew that when he bought his property. Now, he should not be permitted to reverse the course of nature by building an embankment that deprives my place of its natural drainage."

"Why," Henry countered, "should my flowers and vegetables be washed out time and again just to give Overtop's place drainage? After all, the rain fell on his property. He should be made to keep it or drain it safely off elsewhere. I don't want it."

If you were the judge, would you make Henry pull down his embankment?

William Donaldson

Double Take

Ike and Mike were identical twins. When one was arrested for selling liquor illegally, he asked the police to let him go into the next room to change his clothes and leave his keys and money with his twin brother.

When the twin who walked out of the room was brought to trial, his lawyer asked the police if they knew whether it was the twin they had arrested. They were forced to admit they did not.

"How," the lawyer then demanded, "can they tell that the prisoner now at the bar is not the innocent brother?"

"Hogwash!" cried the prosecutor. "We know, because if this man were innocent he would have objected to being taken to prison and tried."

If you were the judge, would you convict the baffling twin?

José Schorr

Juvenile Justice

Because he did not want to risk a murder charge, Muggsy, the holdup man, always carried nothing deadlier than a toy pistol. His favorite was a weighty metal cap gun finished in somber black to look like the real thing.

After committing a series of holdups with his toy, Muggsy was nabbed in the act. Brought into court, he was charged with first-degree robbery with a "dangerous weapon," a crime involving a much longer prison term than second-degree robbery while unarmed.

"Muggsy's cap pistol not only scared his victims, it actually was a 'dangerous weapon' because it was heavy enough to club anyone who resisted," the district attorney argued. "Everyone who ever read a Western has heard of 'pistol whipping' with the barrel of a heavy gun."

"But, your honor," Muggsy pleaded, "surely a toy pistol is no more of a weapon than a rubber dagger or a wooden doll. The way the D.A. argues, almost anything would be a dangerous weapon. Normally, a cap gun isn't, and that is the way the court ought to view it."

If you were the judge, would you regard Muggsy's cap pistol as a weapon?

William Donaldson

Here's Homer's Habitat

In erecting their super ranch house at exclusive Kismet Acres, the Van Pesters carefully complied with the building requirements of the Kismet Development Association. But when they moved in they realized that they had no place for Homer, their enormous St. Bernard dog. So they had the contractor build Homer a handsome doghouse of leftover bricks. It measured seven by five by five feet, and even had a miniature chimney. Officials of the Kismet Development Association promptly protested the "eyesore." When the Van Pesters refused to pull it down, the association went to court.

"The building rules say no structure may be put up without our consent, and that fancy doghouse was certainly built without our consent," the officials said. "So we are entitled to a court order for its removal."

"What is home without a dog?" the Van Pesters countered. "The rules obviously apply to residences and garages. It is ridiculous to try to stretch them to include a doghouse. Kindly leave Homer's house undisturbed."

If you were the judge, would you let Homer continue to live in his dog mansion?

William Donaldson

Do I Have a Deal?

Roger disliked his neighbor Joe. When Joe sought to buy an adjoining strip of land, Roger refused to sell. So Joe had a friend pretend that he was buying Joe's house—thus ridding Roger of an unwanted neighbor—and needed the strip of land to go with the house. Actually the land went to Joe. Roger, learning of this, sued to get it back.

"Joe inveigled me into selling my land by fraud and deceit," Roger argued. "Therefore the whole deal should be declared void and the land should be returned to me. If I had known the true circumstances, I never would have parted with it."

"Roger got the price he asked," Joe replied. "If, in addition, he wanted to prevent my friend from reselling the land to me, he should have said so in the deed. As he didn't, my friend, as the buyer, has the right to sell it to anyone he pleases, including me."

If you were the judge, would you make Joe return the land to Roger?

José Schorr

And the Winner Is. . .

Bertie, an overage delinquent facing trial, was cheered when the state-prison warden agreed that his jailed pal, Joe, could take the day off from prison to testify in Bertie's defense. But when court officers brought Joe to the stand in handcuffs, Bertie recoiled in shock. On being convicted, he demanded a new trial.

"What convicted me," Bertie argued, "was that business of exhibiting my best witness in handcuffs as if he were a public menace. It obviously led the jury to believe the same thing of me. So, I didn't get a fair trial."

"The jurors simply weighed the evidence—not the handcuffs," the state prosecutor sniffed. "We had to take some precautions with Bertie's witness, naturally, in view of the fact that the prison simply lent him to us for the day."

If you were the judge, would you grant Bertie a new trial?

Florence K. Palmer

Money on the Menu

When burglars began dropping into Gus' restaurant almost as regularly as customers, Gus installed an expensive, elaborately wired prowler alarm.

A few nights later another burglar broke into the restaurant and cleaned out every cent of cash without so much as a peep from the alarm. Investigation revealed that it was improperly installed. Gus, in a fury, sued the burglar-alarm company for damages to compensate for the burglary loss.

"You charged me a fancy price for a system to protect my property!" Gus stormed. "Fine protection it turned out to be! You bungled putting it in, so you should pay for the burglary."

"Nothing doing," said counsel for the company. "After all, the burglar might have got away with your money even if the alarm had rung."

If you were the judge, would you order the company to pay Gus?

Bruce M. Jones

Not Quite Van Gogh!

Richard, tired of waiting for the promised renovation of his apartment, timidly asked his landlord's permission to do it over at his own expense. The landlord, thinking Richard a sucker, let him go ahead. But when Richard moved out months later, the landlord was outraged to find that he had used no fewer than three flamboyant hues of paint. It took three paint jobs, instead of one, to redecorate for the next tenant.

The landlord deducted the extra cost from Richard's deposit. Richard sued.

"The purpose of the deposit was to pay for restoring the apartment to its original state," said the landlord, "and due to your outlandish taste it took three paint jobs to do that."

"I only agreed to put on the paint at my own expense, not to pay for taking it off, too," Richard replied.

If you were the judge, would you make Richard bear the repainting cost?

José Schorr

Love Triumphs

With romance in the air, fences meant nothing to Farmer Jones' unpedigreed but vigorous bull. In due course, Farmer Smith, whose pasture adjoined Jones', learned that five of his choicest purebred cows had given birth to calves of dubious ancestry. Jones admitted that his bull had jumped the fence. Smith sued Jones for damages.

"There is no evidence as to how the bull got into Smith's pasture," argued counsel for Jones, "yet we do know that the fence met all legal requirements and the fence was unbroken. Presumably the bull leaped it, but Jones did all that the law required to prevent the beast from trespassing."

"Nevertheless," Smith's lawyer replied, "the law specifically makes the owner of a trespassing bull liable for whatever damage it causes."

If you were the judge, would you make Jones pay damages?

Sarah Morris

"Oilful" Mess

Wealthy Mathilda contracted with a fuel-oil supplier to keep her 3,000-gallon tank filled, and never gave it another thought. For two years the supplier busily kept the tank brimming. Then Luke, next door, traced the damage to his costly trees and shrubs to oil seeping from a leak in the tank. He sued the supplier.

"The supplier was negligent in supplying such enormous quantities of oil without checking to see where it was going," Luke contended. "In two years he poured 26,000 gallons into Mathilda's tank, whereas previously she never used more than 3,000 gallons a year."

"We simply had a contract with Mathilda to keep her tank filled," counsel for the supplier replied. "It wasn't our job or duty to check for leaks. Mathilda never complained that too much was being delivered."

If you were the judge, would you make the supplier pay?

Gerald I. Ralya

Raindrops Keep Falling

The Weatherbees complained to their landlord that they were always soaked because the tenant in the apartment above never drew his shower curtains. The landlord collected damages from the tenant. He did not, however, halt the careless showering or reimburse the Weatherbees for their damages. So they sued him on both counts.

"We're paying for a roof, not sieve, over our heads," they complained. "Our landlord should reimburse us for the damage already done to our place, and also because he failed to stop it sooner."

"The apartment services do not include refereeing disagreements between tenants, and that's what this amounts to," the landlord replied. "I didn't turn on the shower and I'm not responsible for turning it off."

If you were the judge, would you make the landlord pay?

José Schorr

Bus Stop Bungle

Halfway along on Tessie's 200-mile trip on the Flying Goose Bus Lines, the bus driver halted at a roadside restaurant and called, "Lunch stop!" Tessie went in and laid her bag on the lunchroom stool next to hers. When she got up, she found that a sneak thief had stolen it. Then came the unkindest cut—the bus driver refused to allow her back on the bus unless she showed her ticket stub or paid the fare from the halfway stop to her destination. As she could do neither, she hitchhiked home and filed suit against the bus company.

"I paid my fare and the bus driver knew it," she argued. "As a bus company is legally obligated to carry a passenger for the full journey for which fare is paid, the company owes me damages for what it did to me."

"That's true as far as it goes," the company lawyer agreed. "But Tessie overlooks the fact that the company reserves the right to require passengers to produce their tickets or stubs at any time. Drivers cannot be expected to rely upon their memories as to which people have paid their fares. Our driver merely enforced a well-established rule."

If you were the judge, would you make the bus company pay Tessie damages?

William Donaldson

ANSWERS:

Louder than a Lawn Mower

Both Flamms were ordered to pay substantial damages. The court ruled that while the husband is no longer absolute boss of the household, he still heads it to the extent that he must prevent his wife from making a nuisance of herself to the neighbors. If he fails to do so, the court added, he shares her blame.

Based upon a 1951 decision of the Supreme Court of Florida.

Watch Out, Caruso!

The Pottses won.

The court said a landlord "may not foist" an unwelcome stranger upon his tenants in such personal matters as sharing a bathroom or kitchen.

Based upon a 1951 decision of the New York City Municipal Court.

Friendly Persuasion

The evidence was thrown out. The court said that while Francis could waive his constitutional protection against the agents' search under normal circumstances, he was so intimidated by their display of firearms that "his acquiescence was rather in the nature of resignation than consent."

Based upon a 1954 U.S. District Court decision.

Water, Water Everywhere

Henry was ordered to tear it down. The court ruled that lower land is "subject to the servitude of receiving the natural flow of surface waters from higher land." It added for the sake of Henry's garden, however, that he could drain off the waters after they reached his land.

Based upon a 1945 decision of the Kentucky Court of Appeals.

Double Take

The twin, whichever he was, got away. The court ruled that a person cannot be convicted of a crime unless he can be positively iden-

tified as the one who committed it. The ruse of changing clothes was just a "booby trap" for which the police had fallen, the court added.
Based upon a 1954 Missouri decision.

Juvenile Justice

Muggsy lost. The court held that his cap pistol, being a weighty metal object, was capable of being used as a dangerous weapon, even though Muggsy never hit anyone with it. Accordingly, he was guilty of first-degree robbery.
Based upon a 1948 California decision.

Here's Homer's Habitat

Homer and his owners lost. The court said that while a small portable doghouse would not be covered by the rules, Homer's mansion was of such permanent and substantial "size and construction" that the rules applied to it.
Based upon a 1946 New York decision.

Do I Have a Deal?

Roger got the land back. The court said that the basis of the transaction included not only the cash price of the land but the prospect of getting rid of an unwanted neighbor. As there actually never was such a prospect, the deal was void.
Based upon a 1959 Louisiana decision.

And the Winner Is. . .

Bertie won a new trial. The court ruled that a man's witnesses are entitled to appear unshackled. Otherwise, "The old adage that a man is known by the company he keeps could easily inflame the passion, or prejudice the minds, of the jury against a defendant, if his principal witness is kept handcuffed during the trial."

Money on the Menu

Gus lost. Even if the alarm had sounded and someone had responded, the court said, there was no assurance that the burglary would have been prevented. It tossed out, as mere "speculation," the theory that the burglary succeeded because the alarm failed.

Based upon a 1946 decision of the Connecticut Supreme Court of Errors.

Not Quite Van Gogh!

Richard did not have to pay. The court said that the landlord should have expected the tenant to paint the apartment to suit himself, not to suit the landlord.

Based upon a 1956 New Jersey decision.

Love Triumphs

Jones had to pay. The court said that if the law appeared harsh, it was up to the legislature—not the court—to change it.

Based on a 1960 Iowa decison.

"Oilful" Mess

The supplier did not have to pay. The court said he was not negligent, as he did not know of the leak in the tank or the amount of oil previously used.

Based upon a 1959 Michigan case.

Raindrops Keep Falling

The landlord did not have to pay. The court said he was not obligated to "prevent his tenants from annoying each other or from trespassing upon each other's rights." Tenants in those circumstances, it added, should sue the other tenant.

Based upon a 1951 New York decision.

Bus Stop Bungle

The bus company did not have to pay. The court said that the loss of a ticket is the problem of the passenger, not the bus line's. Tickets are good in anyone's hands, it added, so a bus line which consented to transport passengers who lost their tickets might also find itself forced to carry, for free, the persons who found them.

Based upon a 1940 Georgia decision.

Time Out!
Play Ball!

Watch at Your Own Risk

Turk McGurk, pitching star of the Bushville baseball club, was having an off day in a big game. As batter after batter smacked out hits, an especially irate fan bellowed some mean remarks about Turk. Finally he began chanting, "Take out the bum and get a real pitcher."

In a black rage, Turk threw down his glove, spat upon his hands, leaped into the grandstand and gave the noisy fan a thorough beating. When the victim recovered sufficiently to hobble into court, he sued the ball club for damages.

"It is a fine old American custom to insult losing pitchers," he argued. "Turk should have expected it, instead of being so thin-skinned as to beat me up. As he is an employee of the ball club, the club should pay for what he did to me during the game."

"The ball club hired Turk to pitch, not to beat up customers," the club's attorneys replied. "Turk never did wallop anyone before, and so the club had no reason to think he would go berserk. If anyone is to blame, it is Turk personally, not the club."

If you were the judge, would you say a pitcher is entitled to poke a noisy fan?

William Donaldson

One, Two, Three Beans

The sign on the jar of beans in the movie-theater lobby said, "Guess the number of beans here. The fifteen persons who come closest will be eligible to participate in a quiz contest—prize, a new automobile."

A week after Horace entered his guess, he was notified that he was one of the fifteen. The theater had them draw lots to determine the order of questioning; Horace drew No. 1.

Before beginning the quiz, the theater manager announced to the audience that the "contestant last eliminated" would be declared the winner. After three rounds of questions, only Horace and one other competitor remained. Horace missed his fourth question. So did the other man, but being the "last eliminated," he was awarded the automobile. Horace, outraged, sued the theater, contending that he was entitled to at least half the value of the prize.

"He missed his fourth question, too," Horace pointed out. "You should have continued questioning both of us until only one missed, making the other clearly the winner. The way you did it was unfair and a breach of your agreement."

"You were put out first," the theater manager replied, "and that plainly made him the 'last eliminated' under the announced rules of the contest."

If you were the judge, would you give Horace a break?

Bruce M. Jones

Gulliver's Golf Course

Anthony enthusiastically bought a building lot at Divot Acres, a sportsman's dream development combining a golf course and a lake for water sports. But the developer extended the golf course to within fifty feet of Anthony's back door. Then the course was opened to nonresidents, who jammed it and also Anthony's backyard. Anthony sued to make the developer move the offending fourth hole and tee.

"Half of these alleged golfers are such hackers that they hit the ball into my yard and then play iron shots out of my flower beds," Anthony complained. "Low drives endanger my children. Also, the kids get bawled out by golfers, who demand utter silence when about to tee off. One even knocked out my dog with a brassie to keep him from barking."

"Certainly Anthony should be protected from individuals trespassing on his property, but that doesn't mean that the whole club should be halted from lawful use of a golf course which was there when he moved in," the developer's lawyer argued. Then, speaking ardently as a golfer, he added: "To move that fourth tee would spoil the course."

If you were the judge, would you deliver Anthony from the perils of golf?

James A. Eichner

Ye Ole Swimmin' Hole

The river looked so inviting that Buster stopped his car at a public bathhouse for a dip. When Buster dived in, however, a swirl of treacherous currents almost drowned him. He was gasping when rescued. After he recovered, Buster sued the bathhouse proprietor for damages.

"He knew the river was swollen and dangerous, but he let me go right into that deathtrap," Buster argued.

"God made the river, I didn't," the proprietor replied. "I have no control over its currents. All I do is maintain a bathhouse, and no harm befell Buster there."

If you were the judge, would you make the proprietor pay?

José Schorr

Such a Scary Schuss

Angelica took off timorously down the novice ski run at the big state park. Suddenly a large sled darted off-course from the nearby sledding hill and struck wavering Angelica. On recovering from her spill and injuries, she sued the state for damages.

"The state should be held responsible for maintaining such a dangerous combination of courses," she asserted. "While it had posted signs warning sledders to keep off the ski run, that wasn't enough. It should have built a fence."

"The hill," state attorneys replied, "belongs to all the people. Sledders are as much entitled to it as skiers. We did our duty when we warned them to keep out of one another's way. After that, it was up to them to watch out for themselves."

If you were the judge, would you make the state pay Angelica?

José Schorr

The Forgotten "Fore"

Henry, a tennis enthusiast, entered a sporting-goods store to buy a new racket. Near the tennis equipment stood a golfing machine on which golf customers were invited to test their swings with the clubs that were for sale. While Henry was examining a racket, a golfer at the machine behind him picked up a club and whipped it around in a fast backswing. The head of the club caught Henry in the jaw, injuring him severely. When Henry finally got out of the hospital, he sued the store owner for damages.

"You shouldn't have installed a dangerous machine like that where other customers were likely to be," Henry contended. "After all, a store is no place to play golf."

"Nonsense!" said the store owner. "If you hadn't stood so close to the machine, you wouldn't have been hit. Anyhow, you're suing the wrong person. You should go after the man who swung the club. It was his fault, not mine."

If you were the judge, would you exonerate the store owner from all blame?

Bruce M. Jones

Details! Details!

Shad ran his outboard motorboat upstream to within a few
hundred yards of a bend where wild ducks usually could be
found. Then he stopped, lifted the propeller out of the water
and began to unscrew the bolts that held the motor on. He
planned to paddle the rest of the way so as to surprise the
ducks. But the ducks surprised him. Some suddenly flew
toward him. Snatching his gun, he fired and brought one
down. As he paddled over to retrieve it, a game warden swept
up and charged him with violating a Federal law against
shooting ducks from a "powerboat."

"I caught him red-handed, picking up a duck he had just
shot," the warden asserted in court. "As his boat had a
motor attached, it was a powerboat. So I arrested him and
confiscated the duck."

"The warden has probably eaten my duck by now," Shad
said bitterly, "but he hasn't got any case against me. When I
fired, my boat was no longer a powerboat. The propeller was
out of the water, the engine bolts were loosened, and the only
way to make the boat go was to paddle it."

If you were the judge, would you agree with the warden or
Shad?

William Donaldson

Come Here, Little Fish

Suspended lazily near the bottom of a clear little stream, a
school of trout remained unmoved by the assortment of ar-
tificial flies, juicy worms and fat grasshoppers that Obadiah
cast at them in desperate succession. "If they won't bite on
anything," Obadiah growled furiously to himself, "I'll teach
'em a lesson." At that, he cast a large, bare hook into the
school and yanked it through the water until it hooked one. A
warden who had been watching Obadiah thereupon pounced
and arrested him for violating a state law against catching
trout by any method other than "angling."

"Everybody knows you don't fish with a bare, unbaited hook," the warden testified. "I saw this man jerk such a hook through a school of trout until it caught one. That's snagging, not angling."

"The dictionary says angling is 'to fish with hook and line,' " Obadiah countered politely. "It doesn't mention bait as being necessary. Therefore snagging and angling are the same, and I violated no law."

If you were the judge, would you let Obadiah off the hook?

William Donaldson

Strictly Serious Snapshots

Without wearing so much as an eyeshade, nudists of both sexes convened on sunny weekends at a secluded nook. Their privacy was shattered when the sheriff and deputies with cameras raided the place and arrested them. Clothed and in court, they were charged with "indecent exposure of their persons."

"They can't deny the charge, for here are photographs of them parading around without a stitch," the sheriff asserted.

"Both sexes were present, which constitutes indecent exposure. Such goings on shock all decent people."

"Evil to him who evil thinks," the spokesman for the nudists replied. "We are law-abiding folks who sincerely believe in the beneficial effects of sun bathing. That is all we were doing. Our mixed nude sun bathing was in no way indecent or wrongful."

If you were the judge, would you jail the nudists?

William Donaldson

A Good Night's Sleep

At the start of Mortimer's vacation tour through a Western national park, he told his wife and small daughter, "We'll rough it by sleeping outside with nothing but a tent between us, the stars and the bears."

"But, Daddy," his daughter asked, "won't the bears eat us up?"

Confidently, Mortimer replied, "These bears are so accustomed to seeing people that they never bother anybody."

Just inside the park, a Government ranger handed them a pamphlet on how to behave in a national park. Among other things, it said that while bears were bears, they practically never bothered people unless the people provoked them.

That night Mortimer and family pitched their tent, curled up in their sleeping bags and slumbered peacefully until midnight. Then an enormous bear which never had read the Government pamphlet broke into the tent and almost made a midnight snack of Mortimer before other campers drove him off.

On learning that the rangers had received reports that bears had attacked campers a day earlier, Mortimer sued the Government for his injuries.

"The rangers knew that some bears in the park were dangerous," he said, "but instead of warning us, they gave us a pamphlet that made us believe we were safe as long as we left the bears alone. Thus the Government, through its employee's boner, is responsible for my injuries."

"Mortimer can go fan his campfire," Government counsel retorted. "There is no evidence that the bear that attacked him was one of the troublemakers. Moreover, he had no right to assume from the pamphlet that bears, if unmolested, would leave him strictly alone. Every tenderfoot knows that wild animals can't be trusted. Mortimer took his chances and lost."

If you were the judge, would you make Uncle Sam pay for Mortimer's wounds?

William Donaldson

Equestrian Eye Test

Horace, a jockey, rode a nag without being previously introduced to it or its owner. To his horror, the horse insisted on running in a straight line. The track being circular, as usual, horse and Horace collided with the fence at the first turn. Both were injured, the horse suffering a broken leg. Nevertheless, the undaunted nag got up and almost rounded the track, running riderless right in the center. Horace, doubly pained by his injuries and by the horse's improved performance after he left the saddle, sued the owner for $5,000.

"His horse was stone blind in one eye and 'moon-eyed' in the other, and he ought to have told me so," Horace argued. "Instead, he let me try to ride an animal which should have been turned out to graze at an institution for blind horses. So he should pay for my injuries."

"Horace is supposed to be a jockey, but my horse ran better on three legs without him than on four legs with him," the owner replied. "If anything was to blame, it was Horace's riding, not the horse's eyesight."

If you were the judge, would you console Horace to the tune of $5,000?

Arthur L. H. Street

Jaws III

Reggie, a stranger to deep-sea fishing, decided to risk a boat trip offshore. Made confident by a run of some miles through calm water, he persuaded Captain Jack to let him perch in the "pulpit," a hand-railed platform projecting twelve feet from the bow. The captain consented, but failed to warn Reggie of what a sudden wave might do to him. Sure enough, a big

comber swept him overboard. Captain Jack saved him, but
Reggie developed pneumonia. Later he sued because of the
pneumonia and the shock.

"As we set out on a smooth sea, I was completely un-
prepared for what happened," Reggie asserted. "The captain
was neglectful in not warning me of the danger of being
washed overboard, so he should pay damages."

"Reggie, being a big boy, should have realized that he took
a risk in perching in the pulpit rather than sitting safely in a
deck chair," Captain Jack replied. "I didn't warn him
because he should have known he was taking a chance."

If you were the judge, would you rule in favor of water-
soaked Reggie?

William Donaldson

Such a Graceful Dive

Diana's favorite pastime was diving gracefully from the high
springboard at the Dolphin Club. In great contrast, Gus, a
fellow member, enjoyed underwater swimming as much as if
he had been born in a submarine. One otherwise fine day,
Diana's shapely figure sliced through the air and into the
water just at the spot where Gus happened to be cruising a
few feet below the surface. The impact drove him almost to

the bottom of the pool, and injured her. After she got out of the hospital, she sued Gus for damages.

"Gus could have stayed away from the deep end of the pool to avoid endangering those of us who like to dive," Diana argued. "Or at least he should have given some warning that he was playing submarine under the springboard. As he didn't, he should pay for my injuries."

"Ever hear the expression, 'Look before you leap'?" Gus countered. "After all, I didn't run into her. She landed on me like a depth charge. It was up to her to make certain the water was clear before she dived in."

If you were the judge, would you rule in favor of the swimmer or diver?

William Donaldson

STAMATY

ANSWERS:

Watch at Your Own Risk

The fan lost in his effort to collect from the club. The court conceded that Turk was wrong, but said that beating up cash customers was no part of his pitching duties and nothing that the club could have foreseen and guarded against.

Based upon a 1928 decision of the Georgia Court of Appeals.

One, Two, Three Beans

Horace didn't get a cent. The court held that he had no claim unless he could show that if the contest had been otherwise conducted, he, and not the other fellow, would have won it. Actually, the court added, he could not prove anything of the kind.

Based upon a 1941 decision of the Supreme Court of Wisconsin.

Gulliver's Golf Course

Anthony won. The court said: ". . .the tactics of golfers at the tee wreak havoc with plaintiff's comfort and reasonable sensibilities." It ordered the tee to be moved as preferable to "the travail to be suffered by perpetuation of the present method of play."

Based upon a 1959 New Jersey decision.

Ye Ole Swimmin' Hole

The proprietor had to pay. The court said that the owner of a public bathhouse or amusement place is duty bound to warn his patrons of any and all dangers.

Based upon a 1954 Missouri decision.

Such a Scary Schuss

The state paid. The court said, "It is common knowledge that coursing sleds are not easily controlled, while novice skiers are notoriously unable to direct their own movements." Letting them intermingle as the state did, the court added, can result only in disaster.

Based upon a 1941 New York decision.

The Forgotten "Fore"

The store owner had to pay Henry substantial damages. The court held that a store owner owes it to his customers to keep his premises reasonably safe for them, and that he failed to do so when he placed the golf machine dangerously close to other customers.
Based upon a 1932 decision of the Supreme Court of Oklahoma.

Details! Details!

Shad was found guilty. The court ruled that an outboard is a powerboat until the motor is entirely removed from the stern and laid inside the boat. Otherwise, it said, hunters could too easily evade a law intended "to protect migratory birds from an unequal contest" with gunners in speedy powerboats.
Based upon a 1941 United States District Court decision.

Come Here, Little Fish

Obadiah was found guilty. The court, not satisfied with the dictionary definition, turned to an encyclopedia which defined angling as "catching fish by rod, line and hook. . .the salient feature of the pursuit being the allurement of the prey by an attractive bait." It held that a bait or lure is essential to angling, and outlawed "the practice of drawing a line equipped with a hook swiftly through the water with the expectation that said hook will come into contact with some part of the fish."
Based upon a 1925 Indiana decision.

Strictly Serious Snapshots

The nudists went free. The court said their session was essentially a private gathering. It added, "Descending on these unsuspecting souls like storm troopers, the police with their clicking cameras herded them like plucked chickens. There are many a hardy band of sincere and earnest folk among us who insist that all mental, moral and physical health depends absolutely on the regular consumption of vast quantities of bran. Others possess a similar passion for goats' milk. Private fanaticism or even bad taste is not ground for police interference."
Based upon a 1958 Michigan decision.

A Good Night's Sleep

Mortimer was awarded substantial damages. The court held that the rangers' failure to warn him of the bears' unusual misbehavior lulled him into a false sense of security for which the Government was responsible.
Based upon a 1951 decision of a United States District Court.

Equestrian Eye Test

Horace lost his case as badly as he had lost the race. The court said that as a professional jockey he assumed the risk of a spill. And his riding could have been at fault, it added, as there is evidence that a blind horse can be guided more easily than any other.
Based upon a 1950 decision of the Appellate Court of
Illinois, Second District.

Jaws III

Reggie collected. The court held that it is the duty of a fishing-boat captain to safeguard his passengers and to warn them of unexpected dangers, such as rough seas.
Based upon a 1942 Connecticut decision.

Such a Graceful Dive

Diana won. A high court ruled that Gus was indeed a submerged hazard and should either have stayed out of the diving area or have given advance warning of his underwater presence there.
Based upon a 1940 decision of the New York Court of Appeals.

A Family Affair

A Beatific Bet

Ben's uncle hated profanity and poker. Ben, his favorite nephew, was a master at both. To reform Ben, his uncle offered to give him $5,000 at the end of five years if he refrained from cursing and gambling during that time. Ben, who loved money more than anything else, struggled along for five years with nothing more than an occasional "heck" and an infrequent game of solitaire. But when he sought the $5,000, his uncle declined to pay it. Furious, Ben sued.

"Uncle made a legal agreement with me when he gave his word to pay the five thousand, and I lived up to my part of it," Ben said. "In fact, I acted like an angel for five long years. So he ought to pay up."

"You've been sufficiently repaid by the improvement in your habits," the uncle retorted. "Besides, a promise isn't a legal contract unless there's something of value given or exchanged—what the law calls 'consideration.' What you did wasn't of any value to me."

If you were the judge, would you make uncle pay up?

Bruce M. Jones

For a Small Fee

Mrs. Dephew's husband stayed out late at night "on business" so often that she hired a private detective to check up. The detective soon reported that hubby's principal "business" was a blonde. With that evidence, Mrs. Dephew promptly obtained a divorce. Her husband did not object to the divorce or even to paying alimony. But when Mrs.

Dephew sought a court order to make him pay the detective who snagged him, he balked.

"That's going too far," he argued in court. "It's against all human principles to make me pay that snooper's fees."

"You forget," Mrs. Dephew asserted, "that a husband must pay his wife's expenses in a divorce proceeding. This was a necessary expense, for without the detective I might never have found out about your philandering."

If you were the judge, would you make hubby pay the detective?

Bruce M. Jones

It's the "Real Thing"

When Bachelor Bill entered the Army, he made his father the beneficiary of his military-life-insurance policy. Then he met and fell in love with a girl named May. Before they could wed, he was shipped overseas. But his parting words were, "I'll get the war over in a hurry so we can be married."

However, the fighting dragged on and Bill decided to marry his distant love at once, even if it had to be a proxy wedding. Accordingly, May took out a wedding license in her home state of California, hired a minister and had a regular marriage, except that a Red Cross representative stood at her side and made the responses for Bill.

Bill, informed by cable that he was a married man, changed his insurance beneficiary from his father to "my wife May." A few weeks later he was killed. When May applied for the insurance proceeds, Bill's father went to court to get the money for himself.

"A woman can't possibly marry a man thousands of miles away," the father contended. "She never was really his wife, and therefore I am entitled to the insurance money as the original beneficiary."

"I am as true a wife as a man ever had," May replied. "This state, unlike some, does not require that bridegroom and bride stand together in person through a ceremony. Marriage is a contract under which the two agree to take each other as man and wife, and that's exactly what we did in the proxy wedding."

If you were the judge, would you award the insurance to May or the father?

William Donaldson

That Extra Person

Mrs. Jones, a divorcee, rented an apartment with her alimony, but lacked companionship. So she persuaded an adult daughter by a former marriage to move in with her. Immediately Jones objected to paying alimony to support a daughter he never had.

"I'm not required to provide my ex-wife with a bigger home than she herself needs," he argued. "If there's room for another in that apartment, I'm being overcharged."

"Why is he screaming his head off as usual?" Mrs. Jones

inquired. "Am I not allowed to have company without giving a refund? The law requires him to provide me not merely with personal storage space, but a home."

If you were the judge, would you heed Jones' complaint?

José Schorr

Down Mexico Way

Warmly though Pepita loved Zeke when they wed in sunny Mexico, her love cooled in the chilly United States. Returning home on a vacation, she informed her husband she could not bear to go back to the cold *Estados Unidos*. Zeke went home alone and sued for divorce on grounds of abandonment.

"Pepita refuses to return to my bed and board," he pleaded, "so the court should free me to find a mate who does not object to living where I live."

"In this modern age," Pepita replied, "a wife should have as much say-so about where to live as a husband. Zeke can get used to my country easier than I can to his anyhow, and actually it was he who quit me."

If you were the judge, would you grant Zeke a divorce?

José Schorr

Poor Cinderella

Mother had three stalwart sons, but when she grew old and sick, the whole thankless task of taking her in and nursing her devolved on her only daughter. As her last days were painful and trying, she grew to like the daughter less and less, and to idealize her absent sons more.

When she passed away, it was found that in her will she left all her money to the sons and cut off the daughter without a cent. In fact, she added that her daughter had been "disrespectful and unkind." The daughter sued to have the will set aside and a share of the estate awarded to her.

"If my mother had been in her right state of mind and

body," she contended, "she would have known that, far from treating her badly, I was doing all I could for her."

"A woman isn't out of her mind just because she disinherits a daughter whom she dislikes," the brothers retorted. "It isn't just doing things that counts; it's the way they're done."

If you were the judge, would you declare the daughter entitled to a share in the estate?

José Schorr

Too Many, Too Soon

Before marriage, Joe told Julie he believed in "planned parenthood." Trustingly she assumed this meant limited parenthood. But after the marriage, Joe stunned Julie by announcing that his parenthood plan called for at least six children as soon as possible. Terrified, Julie rushed out to get an annulment.

"Even if I did mislead dear little Julie, what's wrong with having a lot of children?" Joe asked. "Isn't that what marriage is for?"

"Joe must have realized that I didn't want a house full of children," Julie sobbed. "So he should not be allowed to beguile and trap me against my will."

If you were the judge, would you free Julie from the bonds of matrimony?

José Schorr

Tic, Tac, Toe

Zinnia tried to remodel Adolph into her idea of a perfect husband. She got control of his salary and put him on an allowance. She objected to his smoking and bowling. She nagged him if he used the mildest cuss word and commanded him never to speak to another woman. One day while gardening, Adolph said good afternoon to a pretty neighbor in shorts. Zinnia bawled him out in a tirade that could be heard for blocks. Adolph thereupon sued for divorce.

"Free me, judge," Adolph pleaded. "I'm rapidly becoming a nervous wreck, with no personality or life of my own, because of her nagging. It constitutes extreme cruelty, entitling me to a divorce."

"Trying to make a better man of a weak-kneed husband certainly isn't cruelty," Zinnia retorted. "It's not as if I broke dishes over his head or beat him with a broom. I take good care of him and cook him three meals a day."

If you were the judge, would you free Adolph?

William Donaldson

Rice Versus Relatives

Papa in his will left money for missionaries in China to feed needy people there. By the time he died, however, the missionaries had been forced to leave China. So his heirs sued to get the money for themselves.

"Those missionaries are now in Hong Kong and Formosa," counsel for the heirs pointed out, "and Papa's will specifically said the money should go to them to help hungry people in China. As that is now impossible, the money goes to the next in line—namely, the lawful heirs."

"Officially Formosa is the only 'China' recognized by the United States Government, and Hong Kong, although actually British, is historically regarded as a part of China," the attorney for the missionaries replied. "Certainly the hungry mouths to be fed in those places are Chinese."

If you were the judge, would you award the money to the heirs?

José Schorr

E'Gads, Ghostly Gamblers

Although Alec's gambling left him well-nigh penniless, he perpetuated his fondness for it even after his death. His will provided: "Nellie and Cora shall shake dice for my diamond ring." This unorthodox precedure was all right with Nellie and Cora, his nieces, but before they could proceed, Cora died. Nellie, as survivor, promptly claimed the ring.

"Not so," Cora's heirs protested in court. "When Alec

died, the ring went to both Cora and Nellie for one of them to become the sole owner by shaking dice. As Cora died before the dice were thrown, the sole owner cannot be determined—so we get Cora's half share.''

"Alec obviously intended one or the other of us—not both—to get the ring,'' Nellie replied. "To sell the ring and split the proceeds is contrary to his will.''

If you were the judge, what would you do with the ring?

Bruce M. Jones

Battle of the Sexes

The men in the Harmony Circle, a social club of both sexes, decided they could have more fun if unhampered by the petticoat influence. Realizing that they had no grounds for expelling the women members, they concluded the next best thing was to amend the club rules so no more women would be admitted. As they outnumbered the women, they succeeded in doing this by a majority vote.

The embattled females retaliated by seeking a court ruling that the new antiwoman bylaw was null and void.

"If that vote passing the bylaw is upheld," they argued, "we women will always be a minority in club matters. Obviously those smart-aleck men hope to make it so unpleasant that we will resign. That amounts to expelling us. They shouldn't be allowed to do indirectly what they have no grounds for doing directly."

The men replied: "A majority vote controls even women when they are in the minority. If they don't like it and wish to resign, that is not expulsion. Resigning is a privilege which they are free to exercise or not, as they see fit."

If you were the judge, would you come to the aid of the ladies in distress?

William Donaldson

The Mighty Money Mountain

In divorcing his extravagant wife, penniless Harry not only agreed to pay her $350 a month in alimony but borrowed $20,000 to give her in return for her promise never to hound him for money again. Ten years later, Harry had saved up $100,000. His ex-wife, having spent her $20,000, asked the court to increase her alimony allowance.

"Her three hundred and fifty a month would be ample," Harry countered, "if only she would learn to stop spending more money than she gets. No matter how much she has, she always spends more."

"Why shouldn't I maintain myself at my old standard of living," his ex-wife retorted, "now that Harry is a rich man? The twenty-thousand-dollar settlement that he made is obviously unfair now that he has a hundred thousand."

If you were the judge, would you make thrifty Harry pay more alimony?

José Schorr

This Teepee's Reserved

Queenie, an Indian woman, fell in love with a white man. They were married and went to live on the Indian reservation where Queenie owned land. Soon, however, her husband received a written order, signed by the three tribal chiefs, saying in effect, "Paleface, go home." The tribe sought the help of the district attorney to enforce its demand.

"As the husband is not a member of this tribe, he is, according to the state law governing the reservation, an intruder," the district attorney argued in behalf of the Indians. "Therefore he must move off the reservation."

"A husband is not an intruder on land owned by his wife," the husband's lawyer maintained. "As an Indian woman has a right to marry a white man, she should also be entitled to live on her own land with him. It is the policy of the law to encourage husbands and wives to live together."

If you were the judge, would you let the paleface hubby stay on the reservation?

Sarah Morris

Sign on the Dotted Line

In most homes the husband buys the insurance. But Betty, who married a convicted thief, applied for her household's theft insurance in her own name. When her house was robbed of jewelry valued at $8,000, however, the insurance company refused to pay. Having learned of her husband's conviction, the company asserted Betty improperly concealed that fact. Betty sued.

"Wives are free citizens and have just as much right to take out insurance in their own names as husbands do," Betty argued. "As the company did not inquire into my husband's past, I didn't feel it was up to me to drag out the fact he had been convicted."

"Betty knew full well that we wouldn't have been crazy enough to sell her husband a theft policy, so she used her own name deliberately to fool us into issuing the policy," counsel for the company maintained.

If you were the judge, would you make the insurance company pay Betty?

José Schorr

ANSWERS:

A Beatific Bet

Ben got his $5,000. The court held that his refraining from cursing and gambling was sufficient consideration to make his agreement with his uncle a legal contract binding on both, even though the uncle *didn't* profit directly by it.

Based upon an 1891 New York decision.

For a Small Fee

The husband did not have to pay. Instead, his ex-wife did. The court held that while a husband must pay for his wife's divorce actions, it would be contrary to public policy to make him finance the cost of detectives to shadow him for divorce evidence.

Based upon 1921 and 1951 Pennsylvania decisions.

It's the "Real Thing"

May won handily. The court held that as her home state had no ban on proxy marriages, May was Bill's lawfully wedded wife and so was entitled to his insurance.

Based upon a 1950 decision of the United States District Court for the Northern District of California.

That Extra Person

Jones won a 50 percent reduction in rent money. The court ruled that, as he was not required to support his wife's daughter, he should not have to pay what amounted to her share of the rent.

Based upon a 1959 Florida decision.

Down Mexico Way

Zeke won. The court said, "If a husband provides a suitable home, the wife is not justified in abandoning it to satisfy her personal preferences regarding climate and customs."

Based upon a 1958 Kentucky decision.

Poor Cinderella

The daughter got her money. The court said that she had done her best by her mother, and the idea that she had been mean to her "could only have been a figment of the mother's imagination." It

added that "wherever it appears that a will is the direct offspring of such a delusion. . .the will ought to be considered no will."
Based upon a 1951 decision of the Supreme Court of Pennsylvania.

Too Many, Too Soon

Julie lost. The court said that "it would be incongruous with the nature of the marital bond to annul a marriage because the husband desires to fulfill one of the primary purposes of marriage, the procreation of the human species."
Based upon a 1958 New York decision.

Tic, Tac, Toe

Adolph won. The court ruled that extreme nagging in effect constituted cruelty. It said: "From the days of Socrates and Xanthippe, men and women have known what is meant by nagging, although philology cannot define it or legal chemistry resolve it into its elements. . . . Prayers avail nothing and threats are idle. Soft words but increase its velocity, and harsh ones its violence."
Based upon a 1947 Nebraska decision.

Rice Versus Relatives

The heirs lost. The missionaries received the money because Papa obviously desired to help the needy Chinese people even though they were not on the Chinese mainland.
Based upon a 1959 Texas decision.

E'Gads, Ghostly Gamblers

Nellie got the ring. The court said Alec meant for it to go to one niece, not to both, and that the only way to do this after Cora's death was to give the ring to Nellie.
Based upon a 1931 California decision.

Battle of the Sexes

The ladies lost their case. The court ruled that it could not interfere with a majority vote unless the effect was to deprive minority members of full use of the club or of their property rights. Such was not the case here, so the bylaw was upheld.

Based upon a 1951 decision of the Supreme Judicial Court of Massachusetts.

The Mighty Money Mountain

The ex-wife got no increase. The court said it would not "penalize a husband's thrift and industry to reward a wife's extravagance." Moreover, it added, it is to the wife's interest "to let him save money which will enable him to continue his alimony payments during his declining years."

Based upon a 1951 Minnesota case.

This Teepee's Reserved

Get out, the court ordered. It ruled that marriage did not give white persons the right to live on Indian reservations under New York State law. The law, it said, represents long-standing public policy to preserve the identity and distinctiveness of the tribes, and to let white spouses stay on reservations would run counter to that policy.

Based upon a 1954 New York decision.

Sign on the Dotted Line

Betty lost. The court ruled that while she was not required to answer "unasked questions" about her husband, she had maneuvered the insurance company into issuing a policy which it ordinarily would have refused to issue.

Based upon a 1957 Federal court decision.

Motoring
Madness

PAUL COKER

Heap Big Hotrod

By the grace of tribal chieftains and the Great White Father in Washington, D.C., the state of New Mexico was permitted to build an expressway across an Indian reservation. Soon after the superzoomway was opened, a young brave was arrested for recklessly ramming another car. Jailed, he petitioned for a release under habeas corpus.

"Your state has no right to jail me," he argued. "Although my people gave the white man the right to construct a road through our lands, they didn't give him the right to police our reservation. On the reservation, which is technically where I was all along, we are not subject to state law."

"How can we maintain and operate a highway without the right to police it?" the state's attorney countered. "When the Indians let us build this highway, they impliedly surrendered their jurisdiction over the land to us. That should entitle us to enforce state law on the highway."

If you were the judge, would you keep the Indian jailed?

José Schorr

Oops!

Mrs. Jones was still thinking how lucky she was to get a seat on the crowded bus, right under the nose of a 250-pound woman who was struggling toward it, when the bus came to a sudden stop. The abrupt halt threw the 250-pounder into Mrs. Jones' lap, injuring her so that she had to be taken to a hospital.

The aggrieved Mrs. Jones sued the bus company.

"We are people, not cattle!" she declared. "We have a

right to expect bus drivers to stop without throwing people off their feet and into our laps.''

"In all our experience,'' the company countered, "we have never been able to find drivers who can stop busses in modern traffic without occasional jerks. That fact is so well-known that most bus passengers hold on to straps, seats and the like. If Mrs. Jones must sue, let her sue the lady who fell on her.''

If you were the judge, would you make the bus company pay crushed Mrs. Jones?

José Schorr

Nitwit Nellie

Everyone doubted that Nellie ever would learn to drive, but after ten easy lessons the instructors at the driving school slapped her on the back and told her to go ahead. No sooner did Nellie step on the gas for her driving-license examination, however, than she rammed a tree. Battered, she sued her driving instructors.

"It was murder to let me think I could drive when I couldn't,'' she contended. "You should have told me.''

"It was our job to build up your confidence, not destroy it,'' the instructors retorted. "You knew better than we did whether you really were capable. Nobody made you believe us.''

If you were the judge, would you make the instructors pay Nellie?

José Schorr

This Way, Madam

Fluttering her big blue eyes, attractive Miss Wyles persuaded the railroad ticket agent and conductor to let her poodle Fifi ride with her rather than in the baggage car. They agreed "this once" because Fifi was such a small, friendly creature. But the train ride made Fifi irritable. She nipped a woman passenger's leg severely. The woman sued the railroad for damages.

"I did nothing to provoke that miserable beast into biting me," the woman said. "The railroad is responsible, because it permitted the beast to ride in a passenger car instead of the baggage car where it belonged."

"Fifi appeared well-behaved," railroad counsel replied. "In the absence of any indication that Fifi might bite, the railroad wasn't negligent and isn't to blame."

If you were the judge, would you make the railroad pay?

William Donaldson

What Price Beauty?

Becky, hit by a car, suffered severe facial injuries. The car owner offered to pay for her wounds, plastic surgery and loss of earnings. Becky, however, held out for more. She insisted that she was entitled to compensation for her loss of good looks due to the accident.

"You have increased the odds against my marrying the man I want," she contended in court. "Possibly nobody at all will propose to a girl whose face has been patched up like mine."

"Why should I pay," the puzzled car owner replied, "because you may not be wooed by suitors who, for all you know, might never have proposed to you in the first place?" If you were the judge, would you let Becky collect?

José Schorr

Quick Exit

Blanche, a timid soul, felt nervous as she climbed into the taxi on a misty dark night. The driver slammed the door and started off in a direction which she believed to be the wrong one. When she objected, he only smiled and kept right on. Soon she began shouting hysterically, "Let me out! Let me out!" And finally, "I'm going to jump out!" The driver said nothing but kept going. Blanche jumped out and was injured. Later she sued the driver.

"It was the driver's duty to stop at his fare's request, regardless of her reason," Blanche's lawyer argued. "By continuing on his way, he imposed a risk of harm on her."

"My client was going in the right direction, so he had no reason to stop," the driver's lawyer replied. "Moreover, she had no real cause to be alarmed."

If you were the judge, would you award Blanche damages?

Sarah Morris

Where are the Pontoons?

Jeffers parked in the only driveway to Art's parking lot and left the keys in his car. To admit another car, Art drove Jeffers' automobile back into his lot, which bordered on a deep river. Unfortunately the brakes didn't work. Art barely managed to jump out before the car plunged into the river. It cost almost exactly the value of the car to fish it out. Jeffers sued for the market value of the vehicle.

"Art should have waited for me to return or else called a policeman to move my car," Jeffers argued. "As it was, he drove my car illegally, without my permission, so he should pay for the damage he did."

"All I did was to shift his car out of my driveway, where it had no business in the first place," Art countered. "I'm not responsible if his brakes failed to work."

If you were the judge, would you make Art pay?

William Donaldson

My Dear Young Man

Miss Hettie, a spinster with very positive ideas as to her rights, bought a ten-cent bus token shortly before the bus company raised the fare to eleven cents and issued new tokens. Not having heard of the raise, Miss Hettie boarded a bus and dropped her old token into the fare box. The bus driver explained the fare rise and asked her to deposit an additional penny.

Miss Hettie refused. After arguing with her for several blocks, the driver stopped the bus and pointedly invited her to pay up at once or get off. She got off, and later sued the bus company for damages.

"Your sale of the old ten-cent token to me constituted a contract entitling me to a bus ride," she claimed. "It wasn't something you could change almost overnight by a fare increase. At any rate, you were not justified in denying me the bus ride."

The bus company replied, "We had permission from the proper public authorities to raise the fare, and it was up to you to pay it. We gave due notice of the raise, and you should have known better than to put the old token in the fare box."

If you were the judge, would you agree that the bus company should catch it in the neck?

William Donaldson

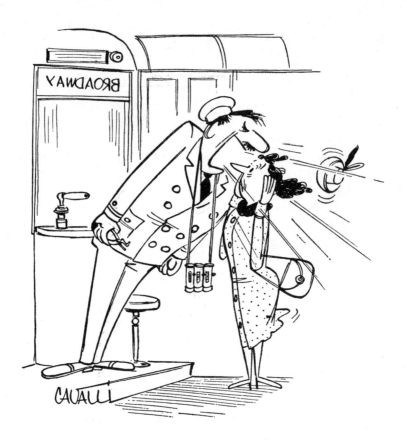

Are You Listening?

As the streetcar slowed down for the stop at which Lulu wanted to change to another car, she asked the conductor for a transfer. Shaking his ticket punch under her nose, he snapped, "You're supposed to get transfers when you pay your fare, not when you get off!" Lulu replied meekly, "I'm sorry—I forgot." Instead of being pacified, the conductor swelled up like an angry bullfrog and began a loud monologue about the stupidity of people who forget to get transfers.

Lulu was so embarrassed by this public scolding that she hopped off the streetcar as soon as it stopped. Unfortunately,

she missed a step and broke her leg. Later she sued the streetcar company for damages.

"Your conductor made a public spectacle of me," she contended. "His humiliating harangue caused the haste which
led to my fall, and you should pay for both my humiliation
and my broken leg."

"We think Lulu was unduly sensitive, but would be willing
to give her a few dollars to compensate for her embarrass-
ment," counsel for the streetcar company replied. "The
broken leg, however, is another story. After all, the conductor didn't throw her off. Her fall was due to her own
carelessness."

If you were the judge, what, if anything, would you do for
Lulu?

William Donaldson

Look Out, Lady!

The absent-minded woman driver parked high on a hillside
without setting her brakes and walked away. A passerby was
horrified to see her car start to roll down after her.

Shouting, "Look out!" he leaped into the path of the

runaway car and pushed the woman to safety. But the car hit him and inflicted severe injuries. So he sued the woman for $2,000.

"I was hurt in saving you from the danger that you brought on yourself," the man contended, "and my hospital bills are a cheap price for you to pay for your life."

"Did I ask you to save my life at that price?" the woman answered ungratefully. "It's nice of you to go around saving people's lives, but there's no law saying they've got to pay you if you get hurt playing rescuer."

If you were the judge, would you say that the rescuer is out of luck?

José Schorr

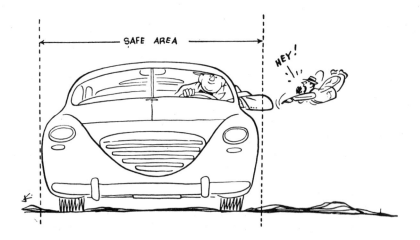

Trucker's Elbow

A motorist was happily tooling along the highway. His car was comparatively new—one of those jobs with little or no running board. As is the custom with many motorists, he was driving with his left elbow jutting out of the window.

From the opposite direction, a couple of trucks approached. The rear truck started to pull out as though to pass, but when the truck driver saw the automobile approaching, he pulled back to his own side of the road. However, the trailer he was hauling swung out and struck the car a glancing blow. It caused only a slight dent in the fender, but practically ruined the motorist's elbow.

The motorist sued for damages, claiming that the trucker, by letting his trailer swing to the wrong side of the road, was responsible for the accident. The truck driver objected, contending that, while he might possibly be responsible for the dented fender, he couldn't be blamed for the crushed elbow, which wouldn't have been injured if it had been inside the car where it belonged.

If you were the judge, would you rule for the motorist or the trucker?

Charles C. Collins

Old-Fashioned Sunroof

Having purchased a rickety secondhand station wagon, Roscoe, a resolute soul, decided not to let its ominous squeaks annoy him. They didn't—until the day when the whole top suddenly caved in on him. Investigation disclosed that termites or other wood-boring insects had completely undermined the woodwork.

A new top, Roscoe found, would cost a pretty penny. As the vehicle was covered by an insurance policy providing payment for "direct and accidental" damages not due to collision or upset, Roscoe asked the company to foot the bill for a new top. When it refused, he went to court.

"Your loss is unfortunate, but it's not covered by our policy," the company contended. "To be compensated, your loss must be accidental. Termites are a pest and a nuisance, but hardly an accident in the accepted sense of the word."

"If having a station-wagon top fall on the back of your neck isn't an accident, what is?" Roscoe retorted. "An accident is something unexpected, unusual and harmful."

"Maybe your neck met an accident, but under our vehicle-insurance policy your station wagon didn't," the company countered.

"Sure, it did," Roscoe insisted. "Those termites got into the woodwork by accident."

If you were the judge, would you define motoring termites as accidental?

Joseph M. Dawson

That'll be a Ticket

After Clarence parked in the metered space, he read the meter notice, DEPOSIT FIVE CENTS IMMEDIATELY, and found he had only dimes and quarters. So he went into the nearest drugstore for change. He returned, nickel in hand, to find a zealous policeman writing out a parking ticket.

"Hold on!" Clarence cried. "I only went to get a nickel to put in the meter."

"Mister, you have an honest face," the officer replied

politely, "but if I believed that story every time I heard it, the parking-meter system would go broke."

In the local traffic court, the officer testified, "There is plain notice on each meter that five cents must be deposited 'immediately.' That means, in effect, payment in advance. Is it asking too much of motorists that they should have a nickel handy?"

"I was doing my best to comply with the law by going to get change," Clarence replied weakly. "I intended to put a nickel right in the meter."

If you were the judge, would you exonerate poor Clarence?

William Donaldson

Tiptoe Through the Ivy

Mr. and Mrs. Blazer, touring cross-country by car and trailer, drove up to Harry's Haven one beautiful evening. As it looked like an ideal trailer park, they stayed. Mrs. Blazer later strolled through the inviting woods bordering the park. By the next day she was in anguish from ivy poisoning. So she sued Harry.

"Harry set up a trailer park and charged a price to use it," she pointed out. "It was up to him to clear away the poison ivy, or at least to erect warning signs. My suffering is due to his negligence, and he should pay for it."

"If Mrs. Blazer doesn't know poison ivy when she sees it, she should stick to the city," Harry replied. "I cleared the trailer park and an area around it. I can't be responsible for what happens elsewhere."

If you were the judge, would you make Harry pay?

William Donaldson

ANSWERS:

Heap Big Hotrod

The Indian went free. The court said the state was given only a "guest's right" to build the highway, not title to the land itself. As the Indians still owned the land, it added, Indians driving on the highway were subject only to tribal and Federal law.

Based upon a 1958 New Mexico decision.

Oops!

Mrs. Jones failed to collect a cent. The court agreed that sudden jerks in starting and stopping busses are inevitable and should be expected by the traveling public. The mere fact that a passenger is injured does not mean that the bus was operated in a negligent manner, it added, although the bus company may be liable for damages caused by an unnecessarily sudden or violent jerk.

Based upon 1941 and 1943 decisions of the Supreme Court of Michigan.

Nitwit Nellie

Nellie lost. The court ruled that as an adult person of average intelligence, she should have known whether or not she could drive. Hence the instructors were not responsible for her accident.

Based upon a 1953 Ohio decision.

This Way, Madam

The railroad had to pay. The court said that while it was not negligent simply in allowing the dog in the passenger car, its employees should have asked whether train rides made Fifi irritable and should have insisted that the dog be muzzled or leashed to its owner's seat.

Based upon a 1940 California decision.

What Price Beauty?

Becky collected. The court declared: "Injury to marriage prospects may blast the money value of a woman's whole life. It is open to every woman, however poor or humble, to obtain a secure and independent position in the community by marriage and, in that matter, which is said to be the chief end of her existence, personal appearance—comeliness—is a consideration of comparative importance with every daughter of Eve."

Based upon a 1951 Ohio decision.

Quick Exit

Blanche won. The court said the driver should have stopped. By
continuing, he only added to her bewilderment and fear.
Based upon a 1946 Massachusetts decision.

Where are the Pontoons?

Art did not have to pay. The court said that all he set out to do was
to shift the car so his lot would not be blocked. It held that he was
not responsible for dunking the car.
Based upon a 1959 Maine decision.

My Dear Young Man

The bus company won. The court ruled that the public buys
transportation tokens subject to properly authorized fare increases.
It said the company was justified in refusing to carry Miss Hettie as
a passenger when she declined to pay the increased fare.
Based upon a 1949 decision of the City Court of Rochester, New York.

Are You Listening?

Lulu collected for both humiliation and injury. The court said that
the conductor's rudeness constituted a legal wrong in itself, and
that he should have known that any person of ordinary sensitivity
might be driven to jump off the streetcar because of his humiliating
language.
Based upon a 1938 decision of the Texas Court of Civil Appeals.

Look Out, Lady!

The rescuer won. The court ordered the woman to pay for his injuries. It said her carelessness not only endangered her own life but
wronged him by creating a situation which led him to risk his life to
save her.
*Based upon a 1946 decision of the Appellate Division
of the Supreme Court of New York.*

Trucker's Elbow

The trucker won this case. The court held that, in letting his elbow protrude from the car at a time when he was passing a couple of trucks on the highway, the motorist was guilty of negligence—that is, he contributed to causing the accident and therefore couldn't collect. Shortly after this decision was handed down, it was made the theme of a safety slogan in a national school-safety-patrol parade:

Don't stick your elbow out too far—
Or it may go home in another car!
See: Pool v. Gilbert et al. Texas Court of Civil Appeals.
No. 11,671—January 29, 1947.

Old-Fashioned Sunroof

Roscoe failed to collect any insurance. A happening may be unusual or unexpected without being an accident, the court maintained. It added that as there was no way of telling when the termites got into the woodwork and began their destructive work, the damage might have been started before the car was insured.

Based upon a 1950 decision of the Supreme Court of North Carolina.

That'll be a Ticket

Clarence didn't get off. The court held that "immediately" meant payment in advance, not after the lapse of even a short time. It said that if it decided otherwise, only those too unimaginative to invent excuses would ever pay.

Based upon a 1942 decision of the New York County Court.

Tiptoe Through the Ivy

Harry did not have to pay. The court said: "The city dweller who chooses to spend his vacation in the great outdoors must, in addition to accepting the fresh air and lake breezes, assume the risks of natural hazards of the outdoors such as flies, mosquitoes, snakes, poison ivy and other natural conditions that would not be found in urban communities."

Based upon a 1958 Ohio decision.

Higher Education

Congested Congregation

One lovely Sunday when the sermon was overlong, the congregation rushed, as usual, from its pews on the first syllable of "Amen!" Faithful Abigail, the only worshiper held entranced by the sermon, moved slowly and was trampled. She sued the church and its officials for damages.

"Those in charge of the church knew that most of the congregation stampedes after long sermons," Abigail argued. "They should have recognized the danger in the situation. Not being prepared to cope with it, they were negligent."

"A church is a nonprofit organization manned for the most part by volunteers," the church attorney replied. "No one has a right to expect it to be run with the smart efficiency of a business concern. Abigail therefore has no real claim."

If you were the judge, would you award damages to Abigail?

William Donaldson

Bingo Bang

Clara was injured at a bingo party in the church hall when a chair collapsed under her. She sued the church.

"While a church ordinarily is immune from suit for injuries suffered during its religious activities," Clara's lawyer argued, "bingo is hardly religious in nature. It is a business activity, and a church is responsible, like any other enterprise, for people who are hurt in such an activity."

"Please, please, a charitable institution such as a church is not liable for injuries caused by negligence," the church attorney replied. "Even though the church may have been negligent, it can't be made to pay."

If you were the judge, would you make the church pay?

James A. Eichner

The Law of Loitering

Although the school system prohibited loitering, Gentleman Johnny was sure it did not mean him. He waited daily in a school corridor for a student friend. After objecting, the principal had him arrested as a loiterer.

"All I was doing was waiting, not loitering," Gentleman Johnny argued. "Loitering in the common sense implies more than lingering or tarrying. It suggests something dirty or besotted. Laws against it are aimed at objectionable individuals who might harm society, not at the public itself."

"Waiting is just another form of loitering, especially when carried to a persistent extreme," the prosecutor countered. "The law does not differentiate between various forms of loitering."

If you were the judge, would you pronounce Gentleman Johnny guilty?

José Schorr

Eck! My Pigtails!

Horrible Henry, aged ten, delighted in pulling his girl classmates' hair and jabbing them with pins. When Principal Smithers spoiled his schoolroom fun with a sound spanking, Henry merely shifted his base of operations and tormented the girls outside the school. Learning of this, Smithers gave Henry another spanking. Henry's parents thereupon indignantly sued Smithers.

"Smithers may have been within his rights in paddling Henry at school, but he had no business to punish him for misconduct elsewhere," the parents contended. "Actually, that second spanking was assault and battery, for which Smithers should pay damages."

"Henry terrorized the girls until their parents hesitated to send them to school for fear they would fall into Henry's clutches later," Smithers replied. "As Henry's parents either couldn't or wouldn't discipline their precious little sadist, I had to do so.''

If you were the judge, would you make Smithers pay damages?

William Donaldson

Former Location

The Upper Upperdunk School Board contracted with Miss Dimity for her to teach at $150 a month, but when she reported she found that the schoolhouse had burned down. Worse still, the board told her that her services would not be needed, as it would take nearly a year to build a new school.

"But don't worry about the children," the kindly board members said. "We've arranged for them to go to another school. Unfortunately, it is well staffed and we can't place you there."

"I'm worried about me," Miss Dimity replied indignantly. "It's too late in the year for me to get another teaching job, I don't know how to do anything else, so what am I to live on if you don't pay me as you agreed?''

"Your attitude pains us deeply," the board retorted. "It's not our fault that the school burned down and you have no place to teach. Do you expect us to pay you $150 a month for doing nothing?"

Miss Dimity thereupon sued the board to compel it to keep its contract.

If you were the judge, would you make the board pay teacher?

William Donaldson

A Present for Me?

When the Reverend Goodbody retired after a quarter century during which he tripled the congregation and built a new church, members of his grateful flock voted him $200 a month as a retirement gift. He settled down happily in a small, flower-covered cottage. Then disaster struck. The Federal Government demanded income taxes on his $200 allowance. Instead of paying, the clergyman went to court.

"That money isn't salary, but a gift which the congregation voted out of gratitude for my years of service," the Reverend Goodbody contended. "It is well established that income taxes cannot be collected on gifts, so make the revenuers stop pestering me."

"The reverend's own argument shows that the money was voted because of his services in the church," the tax collector countered. "As money paid for services is salary and not a gift, the Government is entitled to its tax."

If you were the judge, would you make the clergyman pay up?

William Donaldson

Right Now, "Teach"

Junior, a nine-year-old terror, defied teachers until his school was in an uproar. After all, he shouted, what could they do about it? He found out when an old-fashioned teacher doubled him over her knee and gave him a half-dozen hard spanks. Smarting, Junior fled home. His parents sued the teacher.

"Some children can't be taught without an occasional well-meant spanking," the teacher said. "If you won't discipline your child, his teacher must. The spanking I gave him didn't even break the skin."

"That kind of discipline went out years ago," counsel for Junior retorted. "Children are people and anyone who hits them is just as liable as if he or she hits an adult."

If you were the judge, would you make the teacher pay damages?

José Schorr

This Food is Terrible

Millvale Grammar School installed a cafeteria bossed by a female dietitian, and passed a rule forbidding pupils to lunch elsewhere. Bann O'Bannion, a rugged individualist, snorted and told his two youngsters to eat where they pleased. For lunching at a hot-dog stand across the street, they were expelled. O'Bannion thereupon sued to have the school-lunch rule declared null and void.

"A rule which requires students to eat only at the school cafeteria is unreasonable and dictatorial," he argued. "My children should be allowed to continue in school whether they eat at the cafeteria or elsewhere.''

"The school cafeteria, directed by an expert dietitian, assures the children of a well-balanced lunch which they may not get elsewhere,'' the school officials replied. "Therefore it is to their interest to insist that they use the cafeteria.''

If you were the judge, would you make the children eat in the school cafeteria?

William Donaldson

Whose Right is Right?

Don made an exceptional academic record in teachers' college. In another respect, however, he caused grave concern. A confirmed atheist, he wrote letters to the newspapers asserting his disbelief in God. His professors asked if he intended to teach atheism to pupils. He replied that if the children asked questions, he could not lie about his beliefs. The college refused to graduate Don as a teacher. He sued.

"A college owes a duty to the public not to approve a new teacher who holds fanatical ideas about atheism,'' counsel for the college argued. "Such teachings, if imposed upon the impressionable minds of the young, might work to their detriment and injury.''

"This is the United States,'' Don countered, "and you cannot discriminate against a person for his religious beliefs or lack of religious beliefs. Therefore the college should graduate me.''

If you were the judge, would you award Don a teaching diploma?

José Schorr

Elementary Lineup

Junior, although smaller than his classmates who were throwing erasers, pitched in by retrieving the erasers for them. One hit and hurt a girl in the class. She sued not only the big boys who threw the erasers but also Junior.

"Because he 'passed the ammunition,' Junior was just as much to blame as any of the bigger boys," counsel for the girl argued. "Therefore, he or his parents should be made to pay along with the rest."

"Junior simply picked up erasers after other boys threw them," opposing counsel replied. "He didn't hit or harm the girl in any way. To hold him responsible is ridiculous."

If you were the judge, would you exonerate Junior?

José Schorr

Please Sign my Petition

Irate Elmer objected to nearly everything about the public school that his children attended. So he made up several hundred copies of a list of his grievances. These ranged from objections to paying for school lunches to charges that the teachers were incompetent. Then he marched into a school corridor and passed out his handbills to all comers. The teachers became so upset that they dismissed their classes. The principal called the police. Elmer was prosecuted on a charge of disturbing a public school.

"Elmer was handing out a handbill containing abusive and untrue accusations," the prosecutor stated. "This upset the teachers so that they couldn't conduct classes. Therefore he is guilty of disturbing the school."

"A man has a right to air his views peaceably, and that is all I was doing," Elmer replied. "I didn't actually prevent the teachers from holding classes. In getting excited at my charges, they—not I—disturbed the school."

If you were the judge, would you jail Elmer?

William Donaldson

Disco Dance School

The one thing strait-laced Mr. Green disliked most was dancing; the devil's own pastime, he called it. So when his two young daughters announced that their physical-education class at school consisted of folk dancing, he forbade them to participate. As a result, they were expelled from school.

Mr. Green, mastering his righteous wrath, went to the school authorities and suggested in a spirit of compromise that they form two physical-education classes, one for dancers and one for nondancers. "Nothing doing," was the response. "We're not going to form a special class just for your two children."

Sadly Mr. Green then went to court. "Dancing is against my principles," he testified. "The school has no right to expel my children for something that I'm conscientiously opposed to having them do. After all, I have a say-so in their education and discipline."

"The state law requires physical education and that includes dancing as an exercise," school officials came back. "The way we conduct dancing, not even Mr. Green should regard it as sinful. The folk dances we teach are nothing but healthful fun."

If you were the judge, would you make Mr. Green's daughters take dancing?

Bruce M. Jones

ANSWERS:

Congested Congregation

Abigail loses. The court said churches exist "as places set apart from the material phases of our lives," and that the usual rules of negligence do not apply to them.

Based upon a 1957 Florida decision.

Bingo Bang

The church had to pay. "By conducting the game of bingo as a large-scale money-making proposition," the court said, "the church stepped out of its ordinary and accepted sphere and thereby lost the immunity. . .accorded charitable and religious organizations. . . ."

Based upon a 1960 Ohio case.

The Law of Loitering

Guilty, said the court, because "the animating purpose of the law was not to preserve in our schools a high respectability of visitors, but those minimum conditions of tranquillity and academic repose so necessary to scholastic enterprise. It is not too difficult to imagine the disorder that would result if the public, no matter how innocent their purpose, infested the school halls."

Based upon a 1958 New York decision.

Eck! My Pigtails!

Smithers did not have to pay. The court said that while school officials usually have no right to punish pupils for misconduct except in school, they may do so where outside misconduct directly interferes with the proper running of the school.

Based upon a 1925 Connecticut decision.

Former Location

The board was ordered to pay Miss Dimity $150 a month, even though she did no teaching. The court said its contract could have provided an "out" if unforeseen circumstances, such as the school fire, made it impossible to hold classes. But no such provision was in the contract, and as Miss Dimity was ready, able and willing to perform her part of the bargain, the court ruled that the board must keep its agreement.

Based on a 1918 decision of the Supreme Court of Wisconsin.

A Present for Me?

He did not have to pay. The court ruled that the $200 a month was "a free gift of a friendly, well-to-do group who wished their old minister to live without fear of want." It was not paid for services rendered, the court continued, but was a voluntary "honorarium" which could be terminated at any time.

Based upon a 1954 decision.

Right Now, "Teach"

The teacher did not have to pay. The court ruled that teachers, standing *in loco parentis*, or in place of the parents during school hours, may mete out "moderate correction" as long as it is not done with malice and does not inflict permanent injury.

Based upon a 1954 Alabama decision.

This Food is Terrible

The school won. The court decided that the rule was for the best interest of the pupils. "It is common knowledge that children, if allowed to depend upon their own selection, often indulge themselves in unbalanced diets," the court said. "Furthermore, if uncontrolled at table, young children are apt to engage in rough or uncouth practices and conduct."

Based upon a 1955 Kentucky decision.

Whose Right is Right?

Don lost. The court said that while he had a constitutional right to believe—or doubt—whatever he pleased, he had no constitutional right to teach his thinking to public-school pupils. As Justice Oliver Wendell Holmes put it, a man's right to free speech does not extend to shouting "Fire!" in a crowded building.

Based upon a 1958 Florida decision.

Elementary Lineup

Junior shared the blame along with the rest. The court said he "aided and abetted the wrongful throwing by procuring and supplying to the throwers the articles to be thrown.''

Based upon a 1958 Oklahoma decision.

Please Sign my Petition

Elmer went free. The court said the teachers did not have to accept or read what he handed out, or get so excited about it that they had to dismiss their classes.

Based upon a 1956 Georgia decision.

Disco Dance School

Green won. The court said the school's position—take dancing or be expelled—was a violation of personal rights in cases where the parents were conscientiously opposed to dancing. It told the school to provide some other form of exercise for the children of such conscientious objectors.

Based upon a 1921 California decision.

There are Days Like That

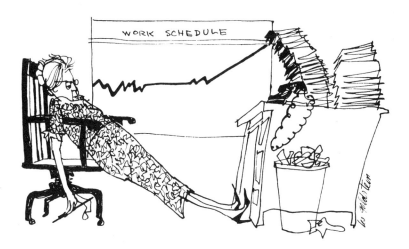

WORK SCHEDULE

It's Been a Bad Day

Barbara, at sixty, was an ideal employee. She went about her duties as office manager conscientiously and efficiently, and did as much work as two average employees. Despite her age, she resented any attempt to decrease her workload. Then hypertension gripped her; she suffered two slight strokes. Next, at the peak of the year's activity, she collapsed with a severe stroke. Disabled, she laid claim to workmen's compensation.

"The nervous strain of running that busy office increased the hypertension and led to her attack," her physician testified. "Thus her condition is directly attributable to what went on at the office."

"She can't obtain compensation just because her condition first manifested itself at the office," her employer's lawyer countered. "We have medical testimony that this would have happened anyhow, sooner or later. And there was no special hazard to her work."

If you were the judge, would you award Barbara the compensation she claims?

Sarah Morris

Pardon Me, Boys

The Army induction officer instructed the draftees to "take one step forward" as their names were called, and said that step would signify their induction into the Army. When reluctant Willie's name was called, he answered present, but did not step forward. After the ceremony, he went home instead of to camp. When the MP's came for him, he went to court for a writ of habeas corpus to retain his freedom.

"The officer himself," Willie argued, "said the step forward is what would make me a soldier. As I didn't take the step, I'm still a civilian and the Army has no claim on me."

Counsel for the Army replied, "The Army isn't being run by childish games. Willie and a hundred others appeared to be inducted, and he was inducted before the whole group as any fool there could plainly see."

If you were the judge, would you say that Willie was in or out of the Army?

José Schorr

Slender Suits Seldom Shrink

When the cleaner returned Hannah's winter suits, she took one look and shrieked. All, she claimed, were woefully shrunken. The cleaner denied her claim, and so she sued.

"Every bit of my clothing was shrunken far too small to fit me ever again," Hannah complained. "Only a circus freak could get into it. Obviously it wasn't that small when I sent it to the cleaner, or," she contended, "I couldn't have worn it in the first place."

"They went back to her in the same size and shape that we received them," the cleaner countered. "It's not our fault if the lady doesn't remember what size she wears."

If you were the judge, would you make the cleaner pay?

Florence K. Palmer

Warmer on Wheels

Mervin, an inventive individual, devised an electric baby-bottle warmer which could be plugged into an automobile dashboard like a cigarette lighter. He did a brisk and profitable business until the Federal Government demanded that he pay an excise tax imposed on the manufacture of "any automobile part or accessory." When he declined, the Government sued.

"My invention is a baby accessory, not an automobile accessory," Mervin argued smartly. "Not by the wildest stretch of the imagination can a baby bottle be regarded as part of a car. The Government is overreaching in this instance."

"As Mervin's bottle warmer is specifically designed to be attached to an automobile dashboard, as a convenience for motoring mothers, it plainly is a car accessory and he should pay the legal tax," Government attorneys replied.

If you were the judge, would you tax Mervin's bottle warmer?

William Donaldson

The Coffee 'n Cream Caper

When the supermarket manager caught Louise stealing a forty-nine-cent jar of coffee, he confronted her with a list of $6.17 worth of items he had seen her steal in the past and he estimated she got away with a total of fifty dollars worth. So he threatened to call the cops if she did not sign a confession and pay up. Terrified, Louise paid him twenty-five dollars on account and promised to pay the rest at the rate of five dollars a week. She paid the first five dollars in the presence of a detective, who promptly arrested the manager for blackmail.

"Why don't you arrest shoplifters instead of honest people?" the manager demanded at his trial. "Louise is the thief; she confessed to stealing at least fifty dollars worth of my store's merchandise."

"You saw her steal only $6.17," the prosecutor replied, "and when you threatened her with arrest for stealing more you committed blackmail—which is worse than shoplifting."

If you were the judge, would you say the manager committed a crime?

José Schorr

The Ring that Annoys

Storekeeper Al ordered 10,000 sales slips bearing his business address and telephone number. By mistake, they were printed bearing the phone number of Jackson, a real-estate broker. Al spotted the error, but continued to use the slips. As a result, Jackson's phone rang constantly with calls from Al's customers concerning their purchases. Jackson sued Al for damages.

"That phone, ringing at all hours, is driving me crazy," Jackson complained. "I asked Al to stop using those slips with my number, but he refused. Now he should pay for ruining my nerves and interfering with my business."

"I'm not responsible for a printer's error," Al replied. "Anyhow, there's no law against having a wrong number on a sales slip, is there?"

If you were the judge, would you award damages to Jackson?

Bruce M. Jones

Devious Dealer Denied

Concerned by a wave of phony "going out of business" sales, the city fathers enacted a law requiring merchants to prove that they actually were closing their businesses before conducting such sales. One staid old merchant who had been going out of business annually for years rebelled. Denied a sales permit, he sued.

"Our purpose in enforcing this law," counsel for the city said, "is to prevent our citizens from being fooled into thinking that they are getting merchandise at sacrifice prices when actually they are getting nothing of the kind."

"If I'm robbing anyone," the old merchant retorted, "there are laws under which you can put me in jail. Until then, I have a constitutional right of free private enterprise to conduct my business as I please. What's more, my going-out-of-business sales are all that keep me in business."

If you were the judge, would you give the perennial merchant his permit?

José Schorr

To Be in Miami

Max, owner of a supercolossal deluxe hotel on a choice Miami Beach site, was undisturbed at first by a project to expand the rival, next-door hotel by a fourteen-story addition. Then he realized with horror that the addition would cast a shadow over his beach for fully half a day each winter season. Foreseeing ruin, Max rushed into court.

"Don't let them put my hotel in the shade, judge," Max wailed. "My guests expect to bask in sunshine all day. The law requires a person to use his property so as not to interfere with the rights of others. If this addition is made at all, it should be in such a way that it doesn't cut the afternoon sun off my beach."

"We're entitled to build what we please on our own property," counsel for the other hotel replied, "as long as it doesn't interfere with Max's legal rights. As for sunshine, Max doesn't own the sun."

If you were the judge, would you permit the hotel to build on the addition?

William Donaldson

Retailer in Kisses

Handsome Harry walked off with Willie's girl right under his nose. Willie, furious, had a printer make up a batch of cards. These he distributed throughout town. They read in part:

"For expert loving call Handsome Harry. Wholesaler and retailer in kisses and hugs. No extra charge for night work. Special attention to other fellows' girls." Smarting under the ridicule of men and the indignation of his girl friends, Harry sued Willie for libel.

"I used to be popular all over town, but now I'm ashamed to show my face in public," Harry said. "Willie's character assassination has wrecked my social life, my health and my business."

"It was just a harmless practical joke," Willie replied. "Harry is trying to make something out of nothing. He knows that all the world loves a lover."

If you were the judge, would you make Willie pay damages?

José Schorr

Tee Time

Eudora, a hard-working blonde secretary, loved golf, but could not afford an expensive country club. So she played weekends on the tax-supported municipal course, paying a nominal fee. One sunny Saturday as she was about to tee off, the manager halted her. He informed her she would have to wait until four p.m., as city council had passed a law barring women golfers on weekends between ten and four. Hell having no fury like a woman golfer scorned, Eudora sued.

"I work during the week just like a man, only harder,"

Eudora argued. "Four o'clock is much too late for me to start golfing. A municipal course should treat men and women alike. As men can play at any hour, the new law discriminates illegally against women."

"You women want all your rights and chivalry too," the city attorney replied. "Actually, women play slower than men and on crowded weekends that slows up things for everybody. The law is a reasonable regulation to keep the gals from poking about and holding up the men."

If you were the judge, would you agree with Eudora?

William Donaldson

huehhergarth

Forget It!

After graduating with high honors in drama, Dorothea worked as a waitress until she got a role acting in summer stock. At the end of the summer she applied for unemployment benefits while hunting another role. But the state refused to pay her benefits, because she declined to wait on tables. Dorothea sued.

"I am an actress, not a waitress," she argued. "They can't force me to wait on tables for a living just because I was desperate enough to do it temporarily on one occasion."

"Dorothea can't turn down good, legitimate jobs which

she is capable of performing, and loaf on the taxpayers' money," state counsel replied. "She is an able waitress and no better than anyone else."

If you were the judge would you let Dorothea collect while refusing to work?

José Schorr

Bargain Basement Sale

Mrs. Bixbee, a fine figure of a woman, undulated into Pardee's Department Store to rummage through a post-Christmas sale, and was delighted by a hat with a veil. Seating herself before a mirror, she put on the hat and pulled down the veil. At that, a hatpin stuck in the veil by a previous shopper scratched her face badly. She sued the store for damages for the pain and medical expense.

"So many women are utterly thoughtless, particularly when they go shopping, that the store should have inspected its hats frequently to make sure that no shopper boobytrapped them with hatpins," Mrs. Bixbee argued. "As it did not, it was negligent."

"We are sorry Mrs. Bixbee scratched her face," store attorneys replied. "But she is blaming the store for what was really the carelessness of some other shopper. The store shouldn't have to pay for that."

If you were the judge, would you make the store pay?

William Donaldson

The Small Print Says

Grudgeon, a sharp bargainer, was amazed and delighted to read in his evening newspaper an ad offering cabinet TV's for only $22.50. Next morning he was at the store before the employees got there. The minute the doors opened he ran in with the ad in one hand and $22.50 in the other.

The salesman took one horrified look at the ad and said there had been a terrible mistake—it should have read $225. "Welshers, hey!" Grudgeon shouted. Publicly goaded, the salesman agreed to deliver the TV for $22.50 as advertised. Grudgeon thrust the $22.50 into his hand and quickly got a receipt. But the store owner, when he heard of it, overruled the salesman and insisted on $225 as the established price. Grudgeon thereupon went to court to make the store sell him a TV at the advertised figure of $22.50.

"The salesman, obviously authorized to make TV sales, took $22.50 and promised to deliver the set," he argued. "Whoever made the mistake in price, I didn't make it. A bargain is a bargain and this court should enforce it even if one of the parties to the deal comes out on the short end."

"A $225 set for one-tenth of its price is too much of a bargain," the store owner replied. "He knew a mistake had been made, and sought to take an unfair advantage of it. I'll gladly refund his $22.50—but that is all."

If you were the judge, would you give Grudgeon the TV for $22.50?

William Donaldson

Unidentified Falling Object

Willie was driving off the bridge when a skidding truck hit the side of the span, bounced up and came down with its left rear wheel inside Willie's bright new convertible. As his insurance policy did not cover collisions, but did cover damage done by falling objects, Willie passed along the repair bill to the insurance company. It refused to pay, so he sued.

"Don't call that collision a 'falling object,' " the insurance company said indignantly.

"That falling wheel missed coming down on my head by only an inch," Willie retorted, "and you try to tell me it wasn't falling?"

"Correct," the insurance company said. "It was a collision just as the dictionary defines it: a violent striking together of two bodies. Most of the impact happened on the same level, and all the damage resulted from collision."

If you were the judge, would you say the truck fell into or collided with Willie's convertible?

José Schorr

It's the Latest Style

Style-conscious George Brummel ordered an expensive fall suit and sport jacket in July for delivery in September. Being loaded with cash, he paid his tailor $400 on the spot. But the clothes were not ready in September, nor October, nor November. Naturally put out, Brummel sued not only for his $400 but for damages.

"The tailor inconvenienced and embarrassed me by not having my clothes ready at the right season," he contended. "He knew that I prided myself on being well dressed, and he let me down."

"As no definite delivery date was set," the tailor replied, "I didn't rush. I'll be glad to return the $400, but pay for Mr. Brummel's wounded pride—never!"

If you were the judge, would you make the tailor pay?

William Donaldson

"Best Costume Goes To. . ."

The Globe Theatrical Players arranged with Speed Railways to haul their stage properties and costumes to the next town where they were to play. They made it clear that they had to have the items sufficiently before the show opened to allow ample time for rehearsal. Instead, the railroad did not deliver the consignment until after opening night. When the players gave the show unrehearsed, and without props or costumes, the result was disastrous. The critics sneered and the show folded. So the players sued the railroad.

"The railroad is responsible for our unsuccessful performance and for the bad press we got," the woebegone actors argued. "Therefore it should pay us damages."

"The show might have been a flop, and criticized as such, even if we had delivered the costumes and props on time," the railroad's lawyer replied. "As damages can't be based on guesswork, we owe the players nothing."

If you were the judge, would you make the railroad pay?

William Donaldson

Million Dollar Mansion

Being temporarily laid off, Sven, an industrious carpenter, spent the time completing his own dwelling rather than idling. The state unemployment board, however, stopped his unemployment compensation. Sven learned he had built a booby trap, not a home. In working on it, the board said, he was self-employed rather than unemployed. Sven objected and sued.

"What difference does it make to the board if I spend my otherwise idle time building my own home?" he asked. "I wasn't self-employed, as I didn't and couldn't pay myself a cent for the work."

"Sven's carpentry developed a property of value to him," counsel for the board replied, "and that amounts to the same thing as paying himself an actual working wage. Our unemployment compensation is to protect against loss of earnings. To Sven it would have been a bonus on top of the home value he earned."

If you were the judge, would you withhold Sven's unemployment compensation?

Florence K. Palmer

Lullaby Time

To lull insomnia victims into sweet insensibility, a sirupy-voiced actor named Erforth made several thousand records of what he called his sleep-inducing monologue. These he advertised as guaranteeing slumber if played at bedtime. When a skeptical United States district attorney tested the record on some eminent physicians, they declared that it was no more of a sleep inducer than many after-dinner speakers. The district attorney then confiscated Erforth's remaining records under a law banning "any device for which false or misleading healing or curing claims are made." Erforth sued to get them back.

"Those doctors want to protect their profession's monopoly in prescribing sleeping drugs," he asserted. "As I make no claim to cure the physical or mental basis of insomnia, the law does not apply to my records."

"Erforth is guilty of false advertising by claiming that his records will wipe out insomnia when in fact they don't," the district attorney argued. "Accordingly, the Government was right in confiscating the records."

If you were the judge, would you give the records back to Erforth?

William Donaldson

The Power. . .ful Promise

The Youngloves bought a dream home from a builder who assured them positively that the heating bills wouldn't run more than twelve dollars a month "even in the coldest weather."

By November, however, the furnace burned a fantastic amount of oil without heating the house. When the builder refused to reinsulate or do anything else about it, the half-frozen Youngloves did the job themselves and sued the builder for what it cost.

"In effect, he sold us an unfinished or inadequately built house, and we had to rip it up and install proper insulation," the Youngloves complained. "Therefore he should pay the difference between what he promised and what he delivered."

"I only gave them my honest opinion of what the heating cost should be," the builder replied. "Beyond that it was a matter of *caveat emptor*—let the buyer beware. There was nothing to prevent them from having a heating engineer investigate and estimate the cost.''

If you were the judge, would you make the builder pay?

José Schorr

Congratulations—It's Yours!

Smedly, shopping around for a secondhand automobile, described what he wanted to a used-car dealer. The dealer told him, "We have a little beauty—clean as a whistle and completely reconditioned. It's a steal at $1,000."

After examining the little beauty from stem to stern, and noting that the speedometer showed only 20,000 miles, Smedly bought the car and drove away happily. Later, however, he learned that the car had been driven 50,000 miles instead of 20,000 and that the dealer had set the speedometer back.

"I've been gypped," Smedly charged in suing the dealer. "The market value of that make and model with 50,000 miles on it is well established as being only $800. I want a $200 refund."

"You forget," the dealer replied, "that we told you this car was reconditioned. Nearly everyone knows that it is customary to set back speedometers on such cars. That isn't crooked, because by reconditioning your car we rejuvenated it so that it was in as good shape as if it had been driven only 20,000 miles. If we had to refund $200, you'd be getting the reconditioning for nothing."

If you were the judge, would you make the dealer pay?

William Donaldson

Soup à la Dress

Just as the waitress came along with a bowl of hot soup, a departing customer suddenly turned and bumped her tray. The soup poured down the back of Eloise, seated nearby. As soon as Eloise could, she sued the restaurant.

"The customer did it, not my waitress," the restaurant owner replied. "So why doesn't she sue him instead of me? We pay for what we drop, but not for what is knocked out of our hands."

"It is the restaurant's business to guard against careless

customers who might inflict harm on other customers," Eloise countered. "Everybody knows that some people in restaurants behave like bulls in a china shop."

If you were the judge, would you make the restaurant pay?

José Schorr

A Poor Party Prank

For an especially gay New Year's party long before the hydrogen bomb was ever heard of, the proprietor of a night club bought some balloons filled with hydrogen. The balloons floated colorfully along the ceiling until very late. Then several of them lost their buoyancy and began to come down.

A young lady had just put on her fur coat to leave when one of the balloons drifted near her head. A sportive companion touched the balloon with a lighted cigar. There was a loud bang. When the smoke cleared away, the young lady found her fur coat badly singed.

She sued the proprietor, contending that he had exposed his guests to danger without giving adequate warning.

Counsel for the defendant replied that it wasn't his client's fault; it was the fault of the dim-witted jokester who poked the balloon with his cigar.

If you were the judge, would you hold the night-club owner responsible and make him pay for the loss of the young lady's fur coat?

Charles C. Collins

Is That Saw Sharp?

After working at it for years, Flordini, the magician, managed to create a perfect illusion of sawing a person in half. Even his professional colleagues were baffled by his feat. It soon made him famous and, by keeping it a closely guarded secret, he rapidly piled up a fancy income from his sawing. Suddenly, however, a motion-picture company somehow learned Flordini's secret and decided to cash in on it by producing a movie revealing every detail of his method.

Flordini, instead of sawing the movie company in half, hurried into court and asked for an injunction to prohibit the showing of the film.

"It will ruin me overnight," he complained. "My continued success depends entirely upon keeping my secret method from the public. To permit this company to expose it for its own gain would be unfair."

"Your secret isn't protected by patent or copyright," the movie company replied. "So, while it may be tough on you, you have no right to stop us from showing your gullible public how you deceive them with your saw trick."

If you were the judge, would you let the movie company reveal Flordini's secret?

Bruce M. Jones

ANSWERS:

It's Been a Bad Day

Barbara won. The court said that compensation is justified if employment aggravates or accelerates a pre-existing disease or infirmity and thus causes disability.

Based upon a 1959 Mississippi decision.

Pardon Me, Boys

Willie retained his civilian status. The court ruled that the draft law required some definite ceremony to transform a civilian into a soldier. As the Army decided to have one step forward constitute the ceremony, and Willie didn't take the step, he wasn't a soldier.

Based upon a 1954 decision of the U.S. Court of Appeals.

(Editor's Note: This case has an out-of-court sequel. Willie was sent another induction notice and was told draft-evasion charges would be filed if he hung back. Willie stepped forward and served his time in the Army, as ordered.)

Slender Suits Seldom Shrink

The cleaner had to pay. The court said the difference in size between Hannah and the clothing was so great that she obviously couldn't wear it. Since she would not incur a bill for clothing already too small to fit her, the court concluded, the cleaner was to blame.

Based upon a 1957 Oklahoma decision.

Warmer on Wheels

Mervin had to pay. The court ruled that the bottle warmer was as much a car accessory as a cigarette lighter or plug-in spotlight.

Based upon a 1958 United States Court of Appeals decision.

The Coffee 'n Cream Caper

The manager was adjudged guilty. The court said it was against the law to use threats and fear to make a debtor pay up "and it makes no difference that the debtor was, in fact, guilty of crime. Furthermore, such conduct results in the concealment and compounding of a felony."

Based upon a 1954 New York case.

The Ring That Annoys

Jackson won. Al's use of slips bearing the wrong number, the court said, constituted "an actual invasion" of Jackson's right to conduct his business peaceably and use his telephone "without unreasonable interference."

Based upon a 1956 Washington decision.

Devious Dealer Denied

The merchant lost. The court said the city was not interfering with his business, but only forbidding him to advertise a sale which might mislead customers.

Based upon a 1958 New York decision.

To Be in Miami

Max lost. The court ruled that a property owner cannot require his neighbors to build in such a way as to avoid casting shadows on his land.

Based upon a 1959 Florida decision.

Retailer in Kisses

Willie paid. The court conceded that "all the world loves a lover," but added that "it scorns the promiscuous lovemaker who preys on the preserves of others, and whose sole ambition is to flirt with frocks." Hence, it said, the card hurt Harry by holding him up to ridicule.

Based upon a 1929 Tennessee decision.

Tee Time

Eudora lost. The state supreme court ruled that laws may discriminate if there is some reason other than sex, race or creed for doing so. Here, it said, the reason was not the women players' sex but their slowness.

Based upon a 1955 New Hampshire decision.

Forget It!

Dorothea lost. The court said that while unemployed persons are not required to take just any old job, "nonetheless, where a person is reasonably fitted for more than one kind of employment, he is not allowed to refuse one kind merely because he prefers the other."

Based upon a 1959 New York decision.

Bargain Basement Sale

The store did not have to pay. The court ruled that "a store cannot be held responsible in negligence for mishandling by customers of ordinary goods placed on public counters" unless such mishandling is clearly dangerous. That usually is not the case, it added, with hatpins.

Based upon a 1955 New York decision.

The Small Print Says

Grudgeon got only his $22.50. The court held that publishing an ad does not technically obligate a store to sell at the price advertised. It said the deal is not final until customer and salesman agree upon a price set by someone in the store who has authority to make prices. Grudgeon's early rush to the store and his badgering of the clerk, the court added, showed that he knew a mistake had been made.

Based upon a 1953 Ohio decision.

Unidentified Falling Object

Willie lost when the court ruled that it was a collision. The court said a "falling object" is one free from suspension or support, brought down solely by gravity. Willie might have had a better case, it suggested, if the truck had fallen on him from a cliff.

Based upon a 1951 Oklahoma decision.

It's the Latest Style

Brummel got back his $400, plus $100 in damages. The court said the garments should have been delivered by fall, "for if not seasonably delivered they would not serve the purpose for which purchased."

Based upon a 1956 Louisiana decision.

"Best Costume Goes To. . ."

The railroad paid. The court said that it was failure by the carrier to deliver the stage items which caused the show to close prematurely "because of poor business."

Based upon a 1958 California decision.

Million Dollar Mansion

Sven lost. The court said that while a man need not sit idle to draw unemployment compensation, Sven did more than odd jobs for petty cash when he completed his home. "The term 'wages,' " the court defined, "means all remuneration from whatever source, including the cash value of any medium other than cash."

Based upon a 1957 Idaho decision.

Lullaby Time

Erforth lost. The court said he was guilty of false advertising. It added that his misrepresentations would lead insomnia sufferers who bought the records to postpone seeking the competent medical advice they might need.

Based upon a 1951 United States decision.

The Power. . .ful Promise

The builder had to pay. The court said that an expert house builder who overpraises his construction to an inexperienced home buyer should be required to make good. It added that it was "investigation" enough for the buyer to rely on the builder's word.

Based upon a 1958 Missouri decision.